P₂　　　　　　'JCA

HELP FOR KIDS!

Understanding Your Feelings About Having A Parent in Prison or Jail

For Kids Ages Six and Older

Carole Gesme M.A., CCDP
with consultation from Michele Kopfmann

Edited By Lisa Schmoker

Beaverton
SCHOOL DISTRICT
TITLE I-A — 503-591-8000
16550 SW Merlo Rd
Beaverton OR 97006

Published by Pine Press, Minneapolis, MN
Copyright © 1993 by Carole Gesme

Designed by: Diane Forbes
Illustrated by: Jack Lindstrom

The Feeling Faces Board, the People Permission Messages, and the Affirmation Feel-O Board are taken from the Ups and Downs With Feelings Game by Carole Gesme, copyright © 1985, 4036 Kerry Court, Minnetonka, MN 55345, (612) 938-9163.

Feeling Pages from HELP FOR KIDS! Understanding Your Feelings About the War — For Kids Ages Six and Older. Copyright © 1991 by Carole Gesme.

"You Can Feel All Your Feelings" is extracted with permission from *Sing Yes! Developmental Affirmation Songs* copyright © 1988 by Darrell Faires, Shalom Publications, 7225 Berkridge, Hazelwood, MO 63042, (314) 521-6051.

HELP FOR KIDS! Understanding Your Feelings About Having a Parent in Prison or Jail — For Kids Ages Six and Older. Copyright © 1993 by Carole Gesme. For information about ordering, contact Pine Tree Press at 4036 Kerry Court, Minnetonka, MN 55345, (612) 938-9163.

Dedication

To the children of the women at the Minnesota Correctional Facility, Shakopee, Minnesota.

This book is also dedicated to D. Jacqueline Fleming, a retired superintendent of the Minnesota Correctional Facility in Shakopee, for her recognition of the importance of maintaining and strengthening family ties while incarcerated.

Acknowledgments

We acknowledge the friends and colleagues who have generously given advice, inspiration and encouragement.

D. Jacqueline Fleming, Connie Roehrich, Mary Scully-Whitaker, Shelby Richardson, Jo Ellen Buzinec, Judy Bolitho, Peggy Beck, Violet, Chris, Lisa, Gail, Beth, Sandy Keiser, Mary Paananen, Nat Houtz, Laurie Perchaluk, Jean Illsley Clarke, Christine Ternand, M.D., Patty Gardner, Kay Joppru, Diane Forbes, Lisa Schmoker, Joy A. Faires and Rodney Verdine.

Thanks to the women at the Minnesota Correctional Facility in Shakopee for sharing their own experiences and their knowledge of the impact of incarceration on families. And a special thank you to Violet, who pushed us to finish this book as quickly as possible for her own children to use.

A special thanks to our families: Chuck, Paul, Ann, Charlie and Thomas Gesme, and Dennis, Peter and Sarah Kopfmann.

TABLE OF CONTENTS

Dear _____ ,
write your name here

This workbook is designed to help you. It is your very own! You can answer the questions by writing words, drawing pictures or talking to someone. A few of you readers will go straight through this book and do every page, or you can choose which page to do at any time. You may want to do some pages many times.

The first part of this workbook is designed to help YOU:

- Learn that your feelings are important.
- Think about your feelings.
- Decide what to do about your feelings.

The second part of this workbook has some activities that you can do to help you deal with your feelings and to have fun.

Remember that there are no right or wrong ways of feeling.

When you keep scared, angry, sad, ashamed or mixed-up feelings inside your body, those feelings can cause an illness such as a stomachache or a headache or bad dreams. They may even lead to fighting and hurting other people. It is important to learn how to let your feelings out so that this does not happen.

You can keep this book as a diary to show how your feelings change. Add as many pages as you need to.

REMEMBER — YOU ARE SPECIAL.
YOUR FEELINGS ARE IMPORTANT.
ALL OF YOUR FEELINGS ARE OKAY.
THERE ARE NO RIGHT OR WRONG FEELINGS.
THERE ARE MANY HELPFUL WAYS TO DEAL WITH
YOUR FEELINGS.
YOU CAN THINK AND FEEL AT THE SAME TIME.

You are unique, and the thoughts and feelings that you express in this book will be unique to you.

**YOU CAN'T CHANGE THE FACT THAT
YOUR PARENT IS IN PRISON.
YOU CAN LEARN TO COPE WITH THIS
SITUATION AND YOUR LIFE.
YOU ARE RESOURCEFUL.**

1

Dear Adults,

We have designed this workbook to help children deal with their feelings about having a parent in prison or jail. (It can also be used for any family member or loved one. Just change the word parent to sister, brother, etc...) Because you are an adult and have a greater understanding of what is happening, children will need to rely on you for information and support; but remember that it is okay to say, "I don't know."

This workbook talks about some of the issues that kids have to deal with when they are separated from a parent by incarceration. Many kids are angry; some are also sad, depressed, scared and ashamed. The purpose of this workbook is to help them identify their feelings and give them information on how to deal with those feelings. It's important for you to understand that your child, or the child that you are caring for, may be experiencing a variety of feelings.

When a parent goes to prison or jail, it is hard on the whole family. For children, questions pile up during the whole process. Three immediate questions that need to be answered when facing this crisis are: Will I be okay? Will my parent be okay? and How will this affect my daily life?

Answer children's questions if you can. Listen to children and reassure them; let them know that you are there to help them face this difficult time and that you care about how they feel. Let your children know that all of their feelings are okay. The pages in this workbook can help you to have honest and open discussions on feelings. Talking about your feelings and their feelings is a good way to express one's self and to relieve tension and anxiety.

Be aware of the effects that T.V. has on children's views of prison and what goes on there. Children watch T.V. differently than adults do. Adults watch T.V. for entertainment, but children watch T.V. to gather information about the world. T.V. provides children with a lot of false information about crime, prisons and violence. Thus, as an adult it is your job to help children figure out what is real and what is pretend. Watch T.V. with them and discuss these things.

Many agencies offer help for kids with problems or kids who are worried about what's going on in their lives. Possible resources may be your child's school or your place of worship. You can ask the staff at the prison or jail for other resources in the community that help families with incarcerated members.

Remember, children overhear adults talking and become confused when they do not understand the whole story. We do not protect children by not talking to them and pretending that nothing is happening. Help your child, or the child that you are caring for, deal with and understand what is happening to him or her. Also, choose which pages in this workbook may be inappropriate for your child because of his or her age — suggest that they skip those.

This workbook may be written for the kids, but you as the parent, or the adult caring for these kids, play an important part in helping them recognize and deal with their feelings.

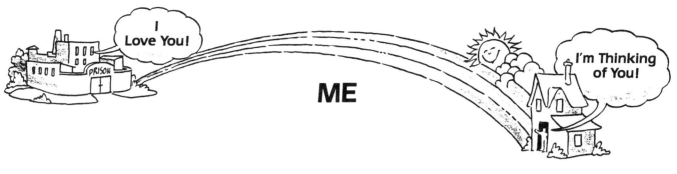

ME

My name _____

Age _____

Where I live _____

Some things I like about myself _____

_____

Some things I'm good at doing _____

_____

MY FAMILY

Every family is special and unique. No two families are alike. Your family is different now because a parent is in prison or jail. Family members do not always live in the same household. Families come in different sizes and ages, and they live in all kinds of places. Families are made up of different people. Some families have mothers, fathers, stepparents, grandparents, sisters, brothers, stepsisters, stepbrothers, a blood brother, a foster parent, an adopted brother, an aunt or many other kinds of people. A family can be you and the people who live with you and take care of you.

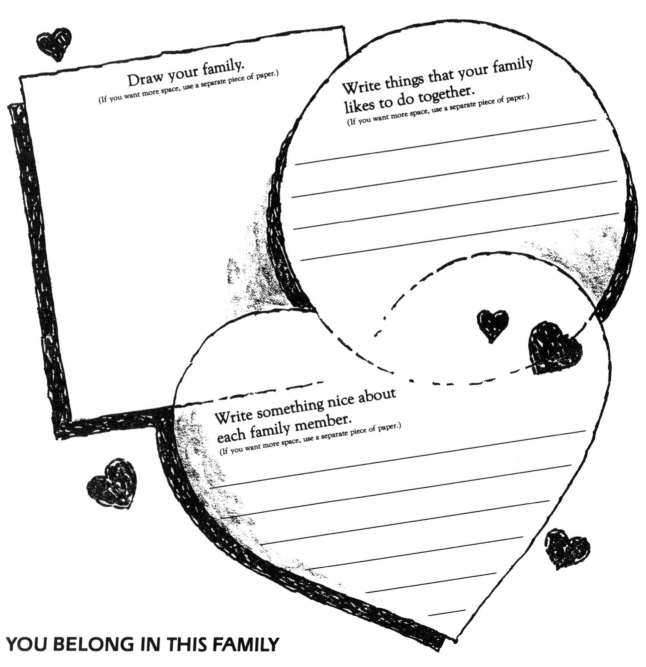

YOU BELONG IN THIS FAMILY

MY PARENT

Someone in my family is not living with me today because he or she is in prison or jail.

Who is that person? _____

Where is that person? _____

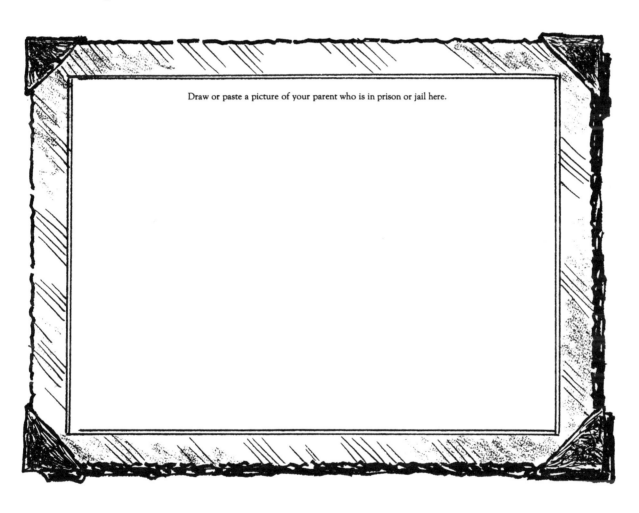

Draw or paste a picture of your parent who is in prison or jail here.

All families have problems. They may be different than having a parent in prison or jail, yet each family has them. Sometimes we feel like our family is the only one with problems. Your family can learn to handle problems in a healthy way, make changes and become closer to each other even when someone is away. Remember, sometimes good people do bad things. Also, it is important to remember that your parent did something wrong — NOT YOU. Just because your parent made a mistake and must go to prison or jail does not mean that he or she is a bad person. Do not blame yourself for your parent's actions. You are a lovable person. Most importantly, your parent still loves you.

LIFE TODAY

Write, draw or tell what is different in your life since your parent went to prison.

Is there an adult I can talk to about this? Who? _____

Do I have a friend I can talk to about this? Who? _____

What is different in your home? _____

_____

_____

_____

_____

What is different in your school? _____

_____

_____

_____

_____

What is different in your place of
worship? _____

_____

_____

_____

_____

What is different in your group of
friends? _____

_____

_____

_____

_____

WHERE I LIVE NOW

Who is taking care of me now? _____

What do I call these people? _____

Where do I live now? _____

Where are the rest of my family members (brothers, sisters)? _____

_____

How long will I be here? _____

Who will keep me safe? _____

How do I feel about all of this? _____

_____

Circle the faces or words that show how you feel or draw your own face in the middle.

MIXED-UP	REJECTED	
SICK	FREE	
MAD	DISGUSTED	
SAD	UNWANTED	
GLAD	TRUSTED	
SCARED	ALONE	
HURT	HAPPY	
LUCKY	DIRTY	
JOYFUL	WORRIED	
NEEDED	FRIGHTENED	
JEALOUS	LET DOWN	
SURPRISED	ALIVE	
SPECIAL	ANGRY	
STUPID	EXCITED	
BRAVE	CAPABLE	
HELPLESS	LOVABLE	
SMART	ASHAMED	
GUILTY	EMBARRASSED	
DEPRESSED	CAREFREE	
CONFIDENT	HORRIFIED	
	STRESSED	

WHERE I LIVE NOW

Your New Home

Webster's Dictionary defines "house" as a structure for humans to live in, and it defines "home" as the lasting place of affections. The actual walls of your house do not make it a home; it is the people inside and their feelings for one another that make a house a home.

It is okay for you to give and accept love from the people that you live with now, and it is okay for you to give and accept love from your parent who is in prison.

Your New Family Can Start Making Your House a Home By:

- **Laughter.** Laugh with your family and friends — laughing is not only fun, but it's good for you, too.

- **Affection.** Tell your other family members how you feel about them. (Ex. "I enjoy spending time with you.")

- **Mutual Respect.** Treat the members of your family with the respect and love that you would like them to treat you with.

- **Be Helpful.** Think of ways that you can help other family members.

- **Music.** Play or sing your favorite songs.

- **Bake.** Bake cookies or brownies. Sit down and eat them together.

- **Play games together.** (See People Permission Feel-O on page 43.)

- **Talking.** Share your feelings with each other.

IMPORTANCE
OF RULES

We all need guidelines as to what we can and cannot do. We need clear and consistent rules in our lives. It is up to you whether you want to follow the rules or want to accept the consequences. However, if you decide to break the rules, be prepared to deal with the consequences (Ex. being grounded).

What rules to you already have in your life? Write down the most important ones.

_____

_____

_____

_____

_____

Why do you think that these rules are important? _____

_____

_____

_____

What do you think should happen when rules are broken? _____

_____

_____

_____

What happens to you when you break a rule at home? _____

_____

_____

_____

What happens to you when you break a rule at school or on the playground? _____

_____

_____

_____

WHO GOES TO PRISON OR JAIL? WHY?

Rules keep us safe. For example, consider what would happen if there were no stoplights or if we simply took whatever we wanted from the store without paying for it.

Society's rules are called laws. When we break these laws, there are consequences that we must accept. Sometimes when a person breaks the law, he or she must go to prison or jail.

What laws are so important that when a person breaks them the person will be punished by going to prison or jail?

_____

_____

_____

_____

_____

If you have any questions about the law that your parent broke, write them here. Find an adult who can answer these questions for you.

_____

_____

_____

_____

_____

**YOU CAN LEARN THE DIFFERENCE BETWEEN RIGHT
AND WRONG — LEGAL AND ILLEGAL.
YOU CAN LEARN THE RULES THAT HELP YOU
LIVE WITH OTHERS.**

What's in a prison or jail?

Write to your parent or ask your parent to describe his or her surroundings in prison. Find the places your parent goes and the people your parent sees while in prison — circle them or color them in.

YOUR PARENT IS SAFE AND TAKEN CARE OF, TOO.

LIFE LINE

How long will my parent be in prison or jail?

Draw the important events in your life that your parent has missed while being in prison or jail on this "life line." Add birthdays by drawing a cake, add Christmas by drawing a tree, etc. . . . .

day parent goes to
prison or jail _____
date

How long will you be separated? ___

_____

What will happen while your parent is gone? _____

_____

_____

_____

What can you do about this? _____

_____

_____

How do you feel?

_____

_____

_____

_____

_____ day parent
date   comes home

YOUR QUESTIONS

You are not alone. Below are listed some questions other kids have asked. Put a star (*) next to the questions you want answers to or write down your own questions. Circle the faces that show how you feel about each question. Ask for help. Find three adults who can answer these questions for you. Use a different color for each question if you want.

Where will my parent eat? _____

What will my parent wear? _____

Where will my parent sleep? _____

Will my parent be safe? _____

What does "behind bars" mean? _____

Can I talk to my parent on the phone? _____

What happens if I get sick? _____

Who will take care of me? _____

_____

_____

_____

> **IT IS OKAY TO HAVE THESE QUESTIONS.**
> **ASK AN ADULT TO HELP YOU**
> **FIND THE ANSWERS.**

I Love You!

PRISON

I'm Thinking of You!

TALKING WITH OTHERS

You need to talk to someone. It is okay to talk to someone about your parent being in prison or jail.

If you are afraid to tell people that your parent is in prison or jail, is it because:
Maybe people won't talk to you, or they'll make fun of you?
Maybe people won't trust you?
Maybe your friends' parents won't let their kids play with you?

This is what some other kids have said about having a parent in prison or jail.....

Name: Connie **Age:** 7	**Thought:** I don't know if my Mom still loves me when she is in prison. **Feeling:** Sad, Scared, Lonely **Result:** When my Mom writes or I visit her, she tells me over and over she loves me and that her love for me won't change.
Name: Yolanda **Age:** 12	**Thought:** I am afraid to tell people my Father is in prison. **Feeling:** Ashamed, Embarrassed **Result:** My Dad has been gone almost two years, and I have learned who I can trust. I only talk to those people about my Father.
Name: Michael **Age:** 14	**Thought:** I worry that my Mom is not safe when she is in prison. **Feeling:** Scared, Worried **Result:** When I visited her at the prison, I could see for myself what the prison was like and that she was okay.

ALL OF YOUR FEELINGS ARE OK

WATCHING
TELEVISION

Write, draw or tell what you've learned about prisons on T.V. Describe how the inmates were treated. Describe what the inmates were doing. Describe what the inmates were wearing. Describe what the guards were like.

YOU CAN LEARN THE DIFFERENCE BETWEEN REAL AND PRETEND. FIND OUT IF WHAT YOU'VE SEEN ON T.V. IS REALLY WHAT LIFE IS LIKE FOR YOUR PARENT IN PRISON. TALK TO AN ADULT.

WATCHING
TELEVISION

When you have a question about what is real or what is pretend on T.V., find an adult who can help you to know the difference.

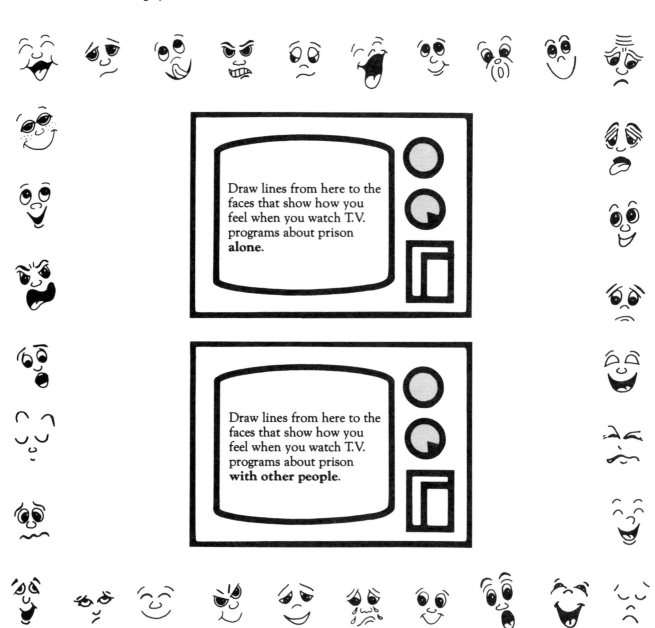

Draw lines from here to the faces that show how you feel when you watch T.V. programs about prison **alone.**

Draw lines from here to the faces that show how you feel when you watch T.V. programs about prison **with other people.**

FEELING
YOUR FEELINGS

When you are worried about your parents, even if you are not thinking about it, your body will let you know. Sometimes we don't feel our feelings. We may store them in our bodies, and our muscles get tight. Instead of feeling afraid, worried, scared, ashamed or mixed-up, we may feel things like stomachaches or headaches. A feeling is your body's way of letting you know that something is wrong and you need to take care of yourself.

Feelings are normal and natural. They are all okay to have. Later we will talk about what to do with them. First, show where you feel your feelings in your body by coloring those areas on the kids below.

TODAY I FEEL

If you feel scared,
what do you feel scared about?

_____

_____

_____

_____

_____

If you feel angry,
what do you feel angry about?

_____

_____

_____

If you feel sad,
what do you feel sad about?

_____

_____

_____

_____

If you feel happy,
what do you feel happy about?

_____

_____

_____

_____

If you feel ashamed,
what do you feel ashamed about?

_____

_____

_____

_____

_____

If you feel mixed-up,
what do you feel mixed-up about?

_____

_____

_____

_____

_____

It's okay to feel what you're feeling! You may be feeling all of these feelings and not know why. Sometimes talking about your feelings and asking questions about your parent being in prison can help.

If you don't know how you are feeling — that's okay — this book can help you.

YOUR FEELINGS ARE IMPORTANT

MIXED-UP FEELINGS

Sometimes we have more than one feeling. For example: Jenny feels sad because she loves her mom or dad and can't be with her or him, but she feels ashamed because she's afraid to tell her friends that her mom or dad is in prison. Sometimes it is hard to know how you are feeling. Draw a face on one child that represents how you are feeling, and then draw a face on the other child that shows another feeling that you have.

Remember —
It is okay to feel more than one way.

PEOPLE

How do you feel about the people in your life today? Are you mad at them, worried about them or afraid that your relationship with them will change?

Use these next few pages to express how you are feeling about these people. Write, draw or talk to someone about these feelings. Add any other people that you want to the list.

Mother/Stepmother/Foster Mother

_____

_____

_____

Father/Stepfather/Foster Father

_____

_____

_____

Brothers/Sisters

_____

_____

_____

Relatives/Grandmother/Grandfather

_____

_____

_____

Police/Guards

_____

_____

Friends

_____

_____

_____

Day Care Provider/Babysitter

_____

_____

_____

Teachers

_____

_____

_____

Principal/Counselors/Bus Driver

_____

_____

_____

Specialized Teachers & Coaches
(For example, piano, soccer, etc.)

_____

_____

_____

Doctors/Nurses/Dentist

_____

_____

_____

FEELINGS

What I Can Do With My Feelings

When I feel **SAD** I can tell someone I feel sad. I can cry. I can ask for comfort and help. I can get support.

When I feel **HAPPY** I can tell someone I feel happy. I can celebrate by myself or with others.

When I feel **ANGRY** I can tell someone I feel angry. I can learn safe ways to express my anger. I can ask for help to solve problems. I can ask questions, gather information and get help.

When I feel **SCARED** I can tell someone I feel scared. I can find safety and comfort. I can ask for information.

When I feel  **ASHAMED** I can tell someone how I feel and what is bothering me. I can ask for help. I can tell someone why I feel ashamed and learn to realize that it is my behavior that is unacceptable — not me. I am okay. I must accept that it is not my fault that my parent is in prison or jail.

When I feel  **MIXED-UP** I can tell someone I feel mixed-up. I can use the Feeling Faces Board in the back of this book to show all of the ways I am feeling. I can ask for help.

YOUR FEELINGS ARE IMPORTANT

FEELINGS

Sometimes we can hide our feelings, and other times (no matter how hard we try) people can tell how we are feeling. It is healthy to show our feelings.

1. **If you are feeling SAD, see page 25 for some things that you can do.**

2. **If you are feeling HAPPY, see page 27 for some ways to celebrate.**

3. **If you are feeling ANGRY, see page 28 for some things that you can do with your anger.**

4. **If you are feeling SCARED, see page 30 for some ideas to help you.**

5. **If you are feeling ASHAMED or EMBARRASSED, see page 31 for what you can do.**

6. **If you are feeling MIXED-UP or CONFUSED, see page 20 for some ideas to help you.**

You can repeat these pages many times.
Your feelings will change from time to time.

SAD ME

When I feel SAD I can tell someone I feel sad.
I can cry. I can ask for comfort and help. I can
get support.

The pain from loss and change is sometimes called grief. Grief comes and goes
like waves.

If you feel sad right now, answer the following questions.

1. I feel sad now because _____

_____

2. What do you usually do when you feel sad? _____

_____

3. Below is a list of things that you can do when you feel sad.
   Check the things that you can do NOW.

- Admit it to yourself. Say, "I'm sad."
- Cry.
- Talk to someone you trust.
- Take a walk.
- Exercise.
- Take a deep breath.
- Be alone.
- Call a friend.

- Ask for a hug.
- Give a hug.
- Talk to your pet.
- Talk to your teddy bear.
- Listen to music.
- Write about it.
- Draw your sadness.

Some of the words below have a similar meaning to sadness. Circle a word and tell a time you may have felt this way.

		Add more words
heartbroken	weep	_____
crying	downcast	_____
glum	grieving	_____
depressed		

Facial expressions communicate feelings without using words. Look in a mirror. Make the expressions shown on this page that show sadness.

Example: frown, pout, crying

How does your body feel when you do this? Think of a time your body felt this way before. Take a survey. Find out what other people feel sad about.

What can you do when others feel sad?

- Spend time together doing something you both enjoy.

- Talk to them about why they feel sad. Listen to them.

- Leave them alone until they feel better.

- Do something nice for them (Ex. make a card, write a note).

- Ask them what you can do to help them feel less sad.

If someone ever yelled at you or called you a baby for crying or feeling sad, that person was wrong. It is okay to cry. It's important to let the tears out. You can find someone safe to share your feelings with.

HAPPY ME

When I feel HAPPY I can tell someone I feel happy. I can celebrate by myself or with others.

Write or draw a picture about some of the happy times that you can remember having with your parent who is now in prison or jail. Copy this page and send it to your parent or put it up somewhere so that you can see it and remember the happy times.

I am happy when I:

_____

_____

_____

_____

Who did you see today that was happy?

_____

How did you know that person was happy?

_____

What can you do right now to help you find happy feelings?

- Practice smiling and looking happy in a mirror. A smile will help you feel better.
- Ask family members what they feel happy about.
- Before you go to bed at night, think about things that make you happy. Let happy thoughts stay in your mind. Say, "I will make tomorrow a good day."
- Find as many words as you can that mean happy. List them. Examples: laughter, joy.

ANGRY ME

When I feel ANGRY I can tell someone I feel angry. I can learn safe ways to express my anger. I can ask questions, gather information and get help.

Here are some things that you can do when you feel angry:

Think about how you are feeling right now. Draw your anger. Show the drawing to someone you trust and share your anger with them. Explain what the drawing means.

It is okay to feel angry. Everyone does sometimes. It is not okay to hurt yourself or other people when you are angry.

We hurt ourselves and other people if we:

1. Kick, hit and bite.
2. Say mean words and hurtful things.
3. Yell at them.
4. Ignore them, or do not speak to them.
5. Hide our feelings — they can turn into headaches, stomachaches or make us tired.
6. Take our anger out on other people.

Instead You can:

1. Tell someone how you feel.
2. Stomp your feet.
3. Throw a ball.
4. Hit a pillow.
5. Work off your anger by getting some exercise, playing a sport or doing something you like.
6. Write down or draw about your feelings.
7. Throw dirty laundry.
8. Tear up newspaper.
9. Ask for a hug.

When someone is angry at you:

What do you do? _____

_____

How do you feel? _____

_____

What do you do when you are angry? _____

Draw a picture of something that you feel angry about.

If you are abused or hit, go to friends, relatives or police. Ask for help from a teacher, school counselor, minister, doctor, neighbor or another adult that you feel safe with.

Sometimes people can get so angry that they become violent. CHILDREN DO NOT DESERVE TO BE HURT. ADULTS DO NOT DESERVE TO BE HURT. If you are ever hurt by someone, find someone else to help you. Write down the names and numbers of people who can help you.

People who can help me:

_____

_____

_____

_____

Police _____ **911** _____

Neighbor _____

Friend _____

SCARED ME

When I feel SCARED I can tell someone. I can
find safety and comfort. I can ask for
information.

Feeling scared often occurs when a family member goes away. Here are some things you can do when you feel scared:

1. **Recognize** what you are scared of. Today I am scared because: _____

   _____

   _____

2. **Share** what you are scared of with someone you trust. Write down the names of three people that you can tell what you are scared of.

   _____   _____   _____

3. **Take Action.** Do something about what you are scared of. Ask questions. Find out as much information as you can about what is scaring you.

   Draw a picture about what you are scared of.

   Have you ever told someone you are scared? What did that person do?

   _____

   If someone ever yelled at you, or called you a baby for being scared, that person was wrong. You can find someone safe who cares about you to share your feelings with.

   Talk about your feelings with others.

   Ask for what you need to help you feel better. For example, I need: a hug, to know ways to be safe or to play.

   _____

ASHAMED ME

When I feel EMBARRASSED or ASHAMED I can tell someone how I feel and what is bothering me. I can ask for help. I can tell someone why I feel ashamed and learn to realize that it is my behavior that is unacceptable — NOT ME. I am okay. I must accept that it is not my fault that my parent is in prison or jail.

Things to do:

1. Tell someone — talk about why you feel embarrassed or ashamed.

2. Admit the feeling. Say, "I feel embarrassed."

3. Apologize. Say, "I'm sorry." Remember that no one is perfect; we all make mistakes.

Shame is a feeling you feel all by yourself, yet you may feel as if everyone else knows what you did. You feel exposed, and you want to run and hide. You feel like you are not good — something is wrong with you inside, and everyone knows and can see it!

Sometimes people feel ashamed for things that other people have done. If you feel ashamed, talk with an adult you trust. Find out if you are the person who did wrong or if someone else is the person who did wrong. You don't have to shame yourself for things others have done.

Write, draw or tell about a time you felt ashamed.

Tell what happened and what you did.

Think about who you can trust (an adult) to tell how you feel. Tell that person about your feelings. For example, when I feel ashamed:
- My face turns red.
- My hands sweat.
- I slump my shoulders.
- I hang my head.
- I don't want to talk about it.

FEELINGS

More Things To Do With My Feelings

1. The People Permission Messages found on page 42 can help you deal with your feelings. Read them and ask others to read them to you.
2. Draw or paint a picture of how you feel.
3. Fingerpaint; use your hands to show how you feel.
4. Draw a picture of your anger.
5. Do something physical. Run, walk, jump up and down, bounce a ball, etc. . .
6. Understand and discuss sounds that bring on feelings (For example: television programs, police sirens).
7. Are there certain smells that bring about certain feelings? Describe what the smells make you think of and feel. Close your eyes and tell what that particular smell reminds you of.
8. Play music. Move to the music, or listen with your eyes closed. How do you feel when you move to the music? Find happy, joyous music. Find angry, sad and scary music, too.
9. Use worry dolls before you go to sleep.

© 1989 Carole Gesme

According to legend, before Guatemalan children go to bed they tell their worries to tiny dolls. Each doll gets only one worry. The child puts the dolls under a pillow, in a small box or basket by their bed. The dolls keep the worries, and the child can sleep soundly.

You may want to try this yourself. If you do, you can copy and cut out the paper people on this page and use them as your worry dolls, or you can draw your own. Use as many dolls as you need.

TAKING CARE OF YOURSELF

Learning to Cope

Sometimes we feel unhappy about how things are in our families.

We can change some things, but some things we can't change. It is important to decide what can be changed and what can't be changed.

We can work to change what we can, but we must let go of the things we can't. Make a list of what you can and can't change.

What I Can Change	What I Can't Change
_____	_____
_____	_____
_____	_____
_____	_____

Children can't choose what happens to them, but they can choose how to act.

If someone makes fun of you because a family member is in prison or jail, you can choose to fight or walk away and not fight. Find someone else to be with. You deserve to be around people who love and support you. Find them.

If kids tease you, ignore them. You can walk away. Here are some ways that you can ignore them:

1. Pretend that you can't hear them.
2. Pretend that they said something nice to you.
3. Say, "Thank you," or "You did a great job on your art project."
4. Change the subject.

Ask for what you need. You might not get it, but that's okay. Not everyone you ask may be able to help you. That's okay, too. Keep trying. You'll find someone who can.

TAKING CARE
OF YOURSELF

1. Say something positive about yourself out loud each day.

2. Feel all of your feelings.

3. Share your feelings when you need to.

4. Ask for help when you need it.

5. Remember that you are not to blame for your parent's behavior. You can't change what they did.

6. You *can* choose how to act (or react).

7. Have fun everyday by doing something you enjoy.

8. Say No — when appropriate.
   Say Yes — when appropriate.

9. If you feel angry at the parent that is in prison, see pages 28 and 29.

10. Exercise with your family or friends. Walking, running, biking and swimming reduce stress levels.

11. Eat and sleep properly.

12. Play with friends.

13. Tell your friends and family members something you like about them.

14. Sing "You Can Feel All Your Feelings" on page 44.

**YOU CAN BUILD YOUR LIFE
THE WAY YOU WANT IT TO BE.**

TAKING CARE OF YOURSELF

There are people that you can talk to about your parent who is in prison or jail. Here is a list of people that you can talk to about how you feel. They may be able to answer some of your questions.

1. A staff member at the prison or jail
2. Your other parent (if available)
3. Your parent in prison or jail
4. A minister or rabbi
5. A school counselor
6. An adult in your family now

> YOUR FEELINGS ARE IMPORTANT.
> YOU NEED TO TALK ABOUT THEM.
> FIND SOMEONE THAT YOU CAN TRUST
> TO TALK TO.

MY WISH FOR
THE FUTURE

Draw your wish for the future.

ACTIVITIES

The second part of this workbook contains activities that you can do to help you deal with your feelings and to have fun.

The activities will help you:
1. Share your feelings about having a parent in prison or jail.
2. Know about words that will help you to understand what the adults are talking about.
3. Get a better understanding of what is happening in your life and your parent's life.

To do this you will use:
1. The words on the Word pages 39, 40 and 41.
2. The Feeling Faces Board on the inside of the back cover.
3. The People Permission Messages found on page 42.

Help With Words

Since your parent went to prison or jail you have probably heard lots of new words. The activity "Help With Words" will help you learn more about what these words mean.

There are several ways that you can use the word pages.

1. You can use the word lists as they are or add more of your own words.
2. You can copy the words and put them on flashcards.
3. You can copy the words, cut them out, fold them and put them in a pile or in a holder.

See the next page to begin the activity "Help With Words."

HELP WITH WORDS

Words — Thoughts and Feelings and Actions

Thoughts

1. Have each family member choose one word by putting his or her initial by it, by choosing one flashcard or by picking a folded word from the pile.
2. Read your word out loud.
3. Share your thoughts about the word.
4. Tell what you know about this word.
   - Where have you heard this word?
   - What do you think about this word?
   - What do you already know about this word?
   - What do others know about this word?
   - Tell a story about this word.
   - Ask an adult about this word.

Feelings

If we learn to talk about and show our feelings honestly and directly we will all feel better.

1. Read your word out loud again.
2. Find a face, or faces, on your Feeling Faces Board that shows how you feel when you hear the word or talk about it.
3. Share these feelings with others.
4. Say the feeling words that fit the faces. Ex: I feel helpless about having a parent in prison.
   Remember: There are no right or wrong answers. No two people feel the same way about the same thing.

Actions

1. Read the People Permission Messages on page 42.
2. Choose one message, or several, that help you to feel better right now. Have someone read the message to you.
3. Turn to page 44 and read the words (lyrics) of the song. Then tell the one feeling you were thinking about when you read the words (lyrics).

Word Page 1

Arrest	Inmate
Siren	Crime
Police car	Jail
Parole board	Halfway house
Workhouse	Work release
Years	Furlough
Months	Canteen
Guilty	Life sentence
Innocent	Death row
Handcuffs	Incarceration
Responsibility	Correctional counselor

Word Page 2

Homicide	Caretaker
Assault	Foster home
Robbery	Social worker
Armed	Guard
Theft	Guns
Burglary	Fence/Wall
Kidnap	Warden/Superintendent
Forgery	Segregation
Arson	Non-contact
Abuse	Visiting room
Sex offender	Visits

Word Page 3

Rules	Police
Uniform	Release date
Staff	Probation
Radio	Parole
Prison	Plea bargain
Cell	Lawyer/Attorney
Bars	Witness
Punishment	Victim
Court	Unlawful
Judge	The yard
Trial	Lock up

PEOPLE PERMISSION MESSAGES

✂ Copy, then cut along lines

You can tell the truth

You can be mad

You know what you are feeling

You deserve love

You can have fun

You are lovable

You can express all of your feelings

You are a terrific person

You can be a good friend

You are important

You can celebrate life

You can learn the rules

You can ask someone to help you

You can do many things

You can think clearly

You are loving

You are special

You can be sad

You can learn new skills

You can be responsible for your behavior

You can keep yourself healthy

You can learn many new things

You can say hello and goodbye

You are kind

You can change your behavior

You belong here

You deserve care

You can help others

You can like yourself

You can be scared

You are capable

You can choose your friends

You can have friends

You can be happy

You can follow the rules

You can say goodbye

PEOPLE PERMISSION FEEL-O

1. Draw individual Feel-O houses or copy the one below for each person. If you do not have a set of People Permission Messages for each person playing, make copies of page 42 and cut out the messages.

2. Each person fills a Feel-O house by placing the People Permission Messages that he or she wants to hear in the blank house.

3. As the leader reads the People Permission Messages out loud in random order, each person removes the ones that he has placed when they are read. The first person to have an empty house shouts, "Feel-O!"

✂ Copy, then cut along dashed lines ---

FEEL-O HOUSE

Permission granted to copy for use with game.

43

YOU CAN FEEL ALL YOUR FEELINGS

Words and Music by
Darrell Faires, Sr.

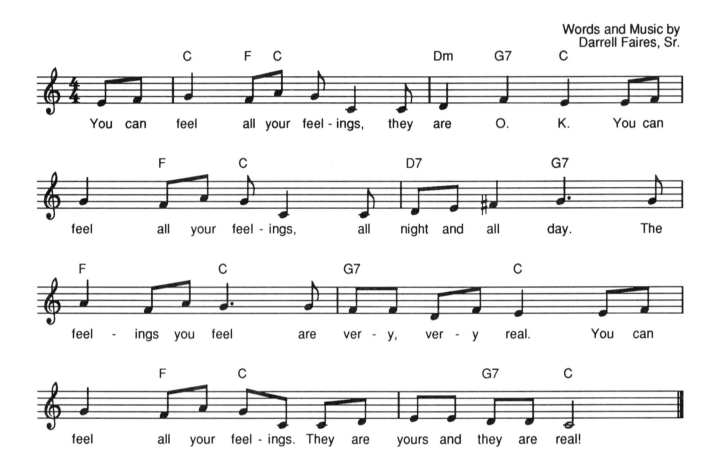

You can feel all your feel-ings, they are O. K. You can feel all your feel-ings, all night and all day. The feel-ings you feel are ver-y, ver-y real. You can feel all your feel-ings. They are yours and they are real!

See the "RESOURCES" page of this book for more "feeling songs" by Mr. Faires.

STAYING IN TOUCH

You can love your parents from a distance. The following are ideas you can use to keep in touch with your mom or dad. Suggest that your mom or dad do some of these activities also.

Memories Box

Keep a memories box. When you remember happy times you spent together with your parent, write it down and put it in the box. At night take one slip out and read it — enjoy the memory.

Write a letter to your parent sharing the memory.

Special Events

Keep a list of special events you celebrate while your parent is gone. (For example: birthdays, holidays, sports events, school programs, etc...) Describe how, where and why you celebrate each event.

Special Event	How Celebrated	Where Celebrated	Who Was There
_____	_____	_____	_____

Draw a picture or write about what you saw on the way to school today. Send it to your parent.

Trace around your feet with a pencil. Have your parent do the same. Compare sizes. Color your feet — draw funny socks on them.

Trace around your hands with a pencil. Have your parent do the same. Compare sizes. Draw gloves on your hands, too.

Send a Picture Letter

Substitute a word with a simple drawing.

Dear ,

I am today.

Watch Me Grow — I've Grown

Items: Tape measure
        Pen

Measure your height on a wall. Each month send or tell your parent how tall you are. Send how much you weigh, also.

or

Take a photo at the same spot on your birthday every year to show your parent how much you have grown.

Write a letter or draw a picture. Cut it up like a puzzle and send it to your parent to piece together.

Create a family newspaper. Have everyone write what is going on in their lives. Then ask your parent to do the same.

Send your parent a cartoon or a funny story that you see in the newspaper.

On your parent's birthday make a card for him or her. Send it to him or her.

Ask your parent to look for signs of spring, winter, summer or fall. Make a list yourself of the signs you see. Who can list the most?

Draw a picture of your parent. List what you love about him or her.

Count down to when your parent gets released. You can make a paper chain of days, weeks or months you will remain separated. Break a piece of the chain each day.

Ask your parent what his or her favorite color is. Write down what you see that day or week that is your parent's favorite color.

Write a question each week for your parent to answer.

Write your parent a letter describing how you look today (Ex. what you are wearing). Tell your parent what you did today. Have your parent write you back and tell you the same.

Send a bouquet of flowers to your parent. You can draw a bouquet or cut flower pictures from magazines to create a bouquet.

Choose a T.V. show both you and your parent enjoy. Make sure it is on at a time you can both watch. Write or talk about it.

Begin drawing a picture but don't finish it. Let your parent finish the picture and have him or her send it back to you.

On holidays write down your favorite traditions. Make lists of people, places and food associated with each tradition. How will it stay the same? How will it change?

Start a family "favorite list." Have each member of your family write down their favorite things. Fill it in and send it to all of the members of your family.

Favorite:	**Category**	**Example**
T.V. Shows	Wonder Years
Foods	Pizza
Movies
Songs
Places
Books

    Add your own categories.

Send your parent a picture of how you feel. Use different color crayons for each feeling you have. You will have a "color picture" of your feelings. Send it to your parent.

Start a story and send it to your parent. Have him or her add on to your part of the story. Continue mailing it back and forth until it is finished.

Draw a picture of your hand. Send it to your parent. Have your parent draw his or her hand holding yours. Tell them to use a different color.

Send affirmations. Choose one people permission message each week. Write down ways you have used the message this week. Have your parent do the same thing. Compare your lists.

RESOURCES

Help For Kids! Understanding Your Feelings About Having A Parent in Prison or Jail
by Carole Gesme (quantity discount).. $9.95
Help For Kids! Understanding Your Feelings About the War
by Carole Gesme (quantity discount).. $5.95
Help For Kids! Understanding Your Feelings About Moving
by Carole Gesme (quantity discount).. $12.95
Help! For Kids and Parents About Drugs
by Jean Illsley Clarke, Carole Gesme, Marion London, and Donald Brundage $10.00
Games *by Carole Gesme:*
The Love Game: A Pathway Out of Shame Into Celebration $36.95
Ups & Downs With Feelings Game — 3 to 6 years......................... $27.95
Ups & Downs With Feelings Game — 6 years to Adult $27.95
Remembering Christmas — 6 years to Adult $19.95
Capture A Feeling (Card Game) — 6 years to Adult $12.95
Keyed-Up For Being Drug-Free — 8 years to Adult $19.95

Additional Tools *by Carole Gesme:*
Affirmation Ovals: 139 Ways to Give and Get Affirmations
by Carole Gesme and Jean Illsley Clarke $6.95
Feeling Faces Paper People... $12.95
Laminated Feelings Faces Board (18" x 12") $2.00
Feelings Faces Stickers (36 faces) $1.00
Pink Permission Messages $1.50/set
$10.00/10 sets
Lunch Bag Goodies — Set of 8 unique note pads for personalizing messages to your children.. $8.95
Self-Esteem Calendar — 12 separate activity month pages for children
(Begin any month — any year) $8.45
Family Books *by Jean Illsley Clarke:*
Self-Esteem: A Family Affair.. $12.95
Growing Up Again.. $14.00
The Decision Is Yours Books (7 to 11 years):
Finders, Keepers *by Elizabeth Crary* $4.95
Bully on the Bus *by Carl W. Bosch* $4.95
First Day Blues *by Peggy Anderson* (Being new at school) $4.95
Making the Grade *by Carl W. Bosch*.................................... $4.95
SING YES! Developmental Music *by Darrell Faires/Shalom Publications:*
SING YES! Sampler (14 affirmation songs) $4.00
SING YES! Songbook (Printed music and lyric sheets of 63 songs)............. $12.50
SING YES! Album (above songbook plus 6 cassettes) $42.50

Prices subject to change.

- -

Mail This Order Form With Your Check Or Money Order To:

CAROLE GESME
4036 KERRY COURT
MINNETONKA, MN
55345
(612) 938-9163   FAX: (612) 935-2038

Quantity	Description	Price
_____	_____	_____
_____	_____	_____
_____	_____	_____
_____	_____	_____
_____	_____	_____
_____	_____	_____
_____	_____	_____

Shipping Charges:

0 to $9.99	$2.75
$10 to $24.99	$4.40
$25 to $49.99	$6.60
$50 to $74.99	$9.30
$75 to $99.99	$10.45
$100 plus	$11.95

(MN residents add 6.5% MN sales tax)

Ship to:
_____
_____
_____

Sub total _____
Shipping _____
Tax _____
Total _____